ALLEY ALLIGATOR SERIES

Alley Alligator
Alley Alligator and the Fire
Alley Alligator and the Hurricane
Alley Alligator and the Big Race
Alley Alligator and the Hunters

Alley Alligator
And The Fire

by Athol B. Packer

Bill C. Cliett

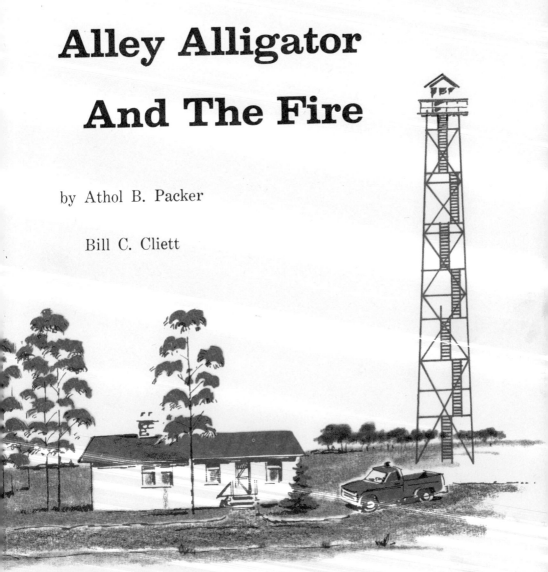

Illustrations by Jim Carleton

BENEFIC PRESS · **Westchester, Illinois**

ISBN O-8175-2002-3

Contents

Up And Out

This is Ranger Ray.
He works in the
Florida Everglades.
He likes to work
in the Everglades.

This is Alley.
Alley is an alligator.
Ray found Alley.
He put him in
this water hole.

Jim and Joe
work with Ray.
Joe was going
up to work.
"I will work
up here," he said.
"I will look
for fires."

"Good," Jim said.
"You go up and look for fires.
"We will go to work, too."
Then Jim said, "Come on, Ray.
"Here are the things you wanted.
"I will put them in."

"Look!" said Ray.

"There is Alley.

"He is not in the water hole.

"What is he doing here?"

"This is not good," said Jim.

"He is too little
to be out here.

"I will get him.

"He can come with us."

Ray called Joe.
"We are going," he said.
"We found Alley out here.
"He will go with us."

Smoke

Ray and Jim went down the road.
Ray got out.
"Look, Jim," he said.
"There is no water out here."

"This is not good," said Jim.
"We must have rain.
"When there is no rain,
there can be fire."

Ray and Jim went
to a water hole.
There was no water in it.

"Look at that," said Jim.
Ray looked.
It was an alligator.
The alligator was looking
for water.

18

Ray and Jim went on.
They were not happy.
They did not see water
for the animals.

"Look!" said Ray.
"Look out there.
"What do you see, Jim?
"It looks like smoke!"
Jim looked, too.
"It is smoke," he said.
"Come on, Ray!
"We must go there.
"I will call Joe."

Fire!

Ray went fast.

He wanted to get there.

Jim called Joe.

"Do you see the smoke?"
he said.

"We are going to look."

"I see it," Joe said.
"I do not like the looks of it.
"Call when you get there."
"Look!" said Ray.
"Look at the animals.
"They do not like this.
"They want to get away."

26

The animals ran and ran.
They did not like the fire.
"I do not like this,"
said Jim.
"It is not good.
"The fire is getting big.
"We must get help."

Jim called Joe.

"We are at the fire,"
he said.

"It is getting bigger
and bigger.

"Get help fast!"

28

"I will get help," said Joe.
"You do what you can."

Help!

Jim and Ray got out
the things for work.
"I will work here," said Ray.
"You work there, Jim."
Jim worked with the water.
The water helped.
Ray helped Jim.
They worked and worked.

"We can not stop the fire,"
said Ray.
"Where is the help?"

"Help must come,"
said Jim.
"I am out of water.
"The fire is getting
bigger and bigger."

"I can see something,"
said Ray.
"Here they come!
"They are coming to help."
"Good," said Jim.
"We must stop this fire.
"We must have help."
The rangers came
with things to help.
They went to work fast.

Where Is Alley?

The rangers worked fast.
They made a fire.

They made a back fire.

The fire was coming fast.

The rangers worked and worked.

Alley did not like the
fire and smoke.
He wanted to find some water.
He got down.
Out he went to find water.

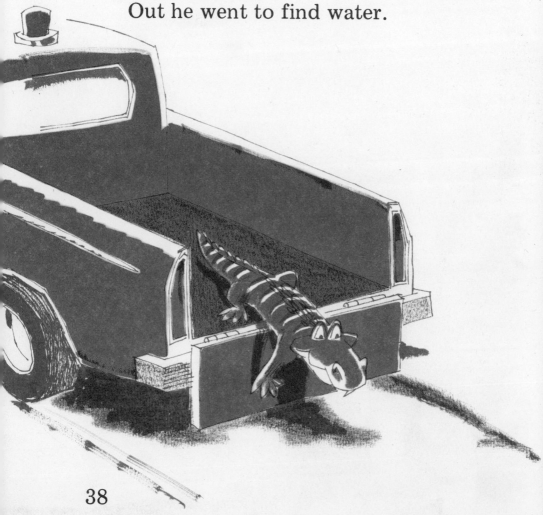

The rangers went on working.
Ray came back to get things
to help stop the fire.
He looked in.
Where is Alley?
"I see," Ray said.
"He went out
when I put the back down.
"He did not like
the fire and smoke.
"Alley must be looking
for water."

Ray looked and looked.
He looked all around.
Ray wanted to find Alley.
He did not see him.

Going After Alley

Ray ran back to help.
He could not look
for Alley now.
He had to help
stop the fire.

The back fire did not work.
The big fire jumped over it.
The fire was coming at Ray.
Ray could not see the rangers.
He could not get back.
He called for help.
The fire was too big.
They could not see him now.

44

The fire was coming fast.
Ray had to get out.
Where could he go?
Then Ray saw Alley.
Alley was getting away.
Where was Alley going?

Ray ran after Alley.
The fire was coming
faster and faster.

Now Ray could not see Alley.
Ray looked around.
Where was Alley?
Where did he go?

Under Water

Ray saw something.
What was it?
It was a hole.
Was there some water in it?
Ray ran to it.
The hole had
a little water in it.
But that was not all.
There was Alley.
He had found the water hole.

Ray was very happy.

Alley had found some water.

Now the fire
could not get them.

"We can not get away,"
said Ray.

"The fire is coming too fast.

"We must get in the water.

"The fire can not get us
in the water."

Ray got down in the water.
Alley went under water.
The fire went over them
and around them.

Ray went under water
with Alley.
He was happy to be there.
The fire could not get them
in the water.

Then Ray came up.
He looked around.
There was no fire
around the hole now.
It was black
around the water hole.

The Big Surprise

Ray jumped up.
He saw Jim coming.
Jim was looking for him.
"Here I am, Jim!" he said.
"Here I am!"
Jim came up.
"Where were you?" he said.
"I looked and looked for you.
"I could not find you.
"I did not want the fire
to get you."

"I was in there," Ray said.
"Alley found a water hole.
"We got in the water.
"The fire could not get us."

"Look!" said Jim.
"It is getting very black.
"It is going to rain.
"The rain will help
put out the fire."

Down came the rain.
It rained and rained.
The rain put out the fire.
That made the rangers
very happy.

The rangers ran and laughed
in the rain.

It was funny to see them
jumping in the water.

Jim looked at Ray.

"Now we look like you,"
he laughed.

"We are in water, too."

The work was over.
Jim called Joe.
"The fire is out," he said.
"We are coming back."

Ray and Jim were surprised
when they got back.
All the rangers were there.
The rangers had a party
for Alley.
"Alley helped in the fire,"
they laughed.
"He found the water hole
for Ray.
"Now he can be a ranger, too."

Vocabulary

The total vocabulary of this book is one hundred four words, excluding proper names and sound words. The fifty words in roman type may be familiar to children reading on a primer level. The nine words above primer level are shown in italic type. The number indicates the page on which the word first appears.

after 46
all 40
alligator 8
an 8
animals 19
around 40
at 18

back 39
be 13
bigger 28
black 55
but 48

call(ed) 14
came 34
could 41

do(ing) 13

fast(er) 22
fire(s) 9
found 8
funny 61

get(ting) 13
going 9
got 15

had 41
happy 19
help(ed) 27
him 8
hole 8

laugh(ed) 61

made 36
must 16

no 15
now 41

of 25
out 13
over 42

party 63
put 8

rain(ed) 16
rangers 34
road 15

smoke 21
some 38
something 34
stop 32
surprise(d) 63

that 18
them 11
then 45
there 13
thing 11

under 52
us 13

very 51

was 9
water 8
were 19
when 16
work(ed) 7